CW00377183

Don't give
successfully combating "orange-peel" skin
cellulite a chance

PLEASE PINCH

Do you want to stop unattractive dimples appearing on your thighs or bottom? Or perhaps you already have those little lumps, or they are beginning to grow? Do a pinch test now: squeeze the skin on your thigh between your finger and thumb. If slight dimples appear, now is the time to do something to stop cellulite developing. Even if no dimples appear, it can do no harm to take preventative action. Let's be clear right from the start: that infamous "orange-peel" skin is how cellulite, often wrongly called cellulitis, manifests itself.

Cellulite is made up of the fat deposits in the subcutaneous fatty tissue, which press up against the epidermis from below and appear in the form of unattractive dimples. Waste products were believed to be responsible for cellulite, but research in the USA has shown that cellulite is "merely" fat. The areas most frequently affected are the thighs and buttocks, but that characteristic orange-peel skin can also occur on the hips, stomach, and upper arms.

The typical woman

Cellulite can affect any woman, and many women under 30 already have orange-peel skin to a greater or lesser extent.

Why do men rarely get cellulite? In the parts of the body susceptible to orange-peel skin, women have large fat pockets, loosely held together by connective tissue. They can accommodate a lot of fat and can stretch considerably. If during the ageing process this connective tissue becomes weaker and the skin above it becomes less elastic, this fatty padding can appear as small lumps beneath the skin. In men, the fat pockets in the hypodermis are small and are usually held firmly in place by overlapping cords of connective tissue.

Not God-given

It is true that cellulite can affect any woman – but it doesn't have to. A balanced and, most importantly, low-fat diet, combined with an adequate liquid intake, will prevent those unattractive dimples forming. Such a diet has nothing to do with making sacrifices, and everything to do with choosing and preparing food wisely. Enjoy!

Exercise is just as important. People who exercise regularly are generally free from orange-peel skin. Athletes rarely have any excess weight on them, and their connective tissue is and will remain wonderfully firm. Their muscle layer is stronger, while the fatty cells are small.

Regular exercise and daily massage also help in the battle against cellulite, enabling you to work on your own personal weak points. Hot-and-cold showers are very beneficial, improving the blood supply to the affected areas and stimulating the local metabolism. Expensive anti-cellulite creams are of limited value however, and of real benefit only to the manufacturer. Time and again, research has shown that such creams have no obvious effect.

Do you know your BMI?

Correct nutrition is still the best weapon in the battle against cellulite. To do something positive to combat your orange-peel skin, you will also have to deal with excess weight and fatty padding. But do you really have too much weight around your midriff? For a quick check use the simple formula:

normal weight (kg) = height in cm − 100

Experts now work with the Body Mass Index (BMI), which relates body weight to body size. To calculate your BMI use the formula:

$$\frac{\text{weight (kg)}}{\text{height (m) x height (m)}}$$

The value should be between 20 and 25. Less than 20 shows that you are underweight; over 25 means that you are carrying a few extra pounds.

Less fat means less

the wonderfully simple recipe for success

orange-peel skin

GO EASY ON FAT

To reduce fatty subcutaneous tissue, there is one part of your diet you need to cut back on above all: fat intake. But let's not disparage fat totally – you need it to remain healthy and it has an important part to play in making food tasty. Use the right fat and enjoy it sparingly. When trying to lose weight, limit yourself to 40–50g daily, equivalent to 4–5 tablespoons of oil.

JUST CROSS FAT OFF YOUR LIST

✱ Small (!) quantities of butter or vegetable oil margarine with a high nutritive value are good for spreading on bread.

✱ Cold-pressed vegetable oils, such as rapeseed, safflower, or sunflower oil, are best for salads. Nut oils are also good and make for a healthy change.

✱ Extra virgin olive oil is excellent for cooking and frying.

✱ You can do a lot for your fat balance just by drawing up a carefully considered shopping list.

* Avoid too many fat-rich foods such as deep-fried dishes, cream soups, crisps, or chocolate.

* Fatty foods should always play only a secondary role in your diet. Low-calorie food should hold centre stage: enjoy tucking into fruit, vegetables and salads, potatoes, rice, and pasta. They are low in calories, yet full of valuable vitamins and minerals.

CAREFUL LOW-FAT COOKING IS THE ANSWER

Use fat sparingly when preparing food. Many foods can be fried or cooked without adding any extra oil. Buy a good non-stick frying pan and/or a wok for (practically) fat-free frying, or grill food instead. Vegetables are best braised (cooked with only a little liquid in a tightly covered pan) or steamed (cooked in water vapour). This way, vitamins and minerals are not lost. Instead of disappearing into the water or the air, they end up on your plate and thus at their intended destination.

Cooking food in aluminium foil or an earthenware pot is another good method. Do not add any fat, so that healthy foods stay as healthy as possible, firmly sealed in the foil or pot.

IS IT REALLY A LOW-FAT FOOD?

FOOD	FAT CONTENT PER 100g	CALORIES PER 100g
Milk, 3.5% fat	3.5g	64
Milk, 1.5% fat	1.5g	47
Milk, skimmed	0.1g	35
Buttermilk	0.5g	35
Soured cream, 10% fat	10g	123
Whipping cream, 30% fat	31.7g	309
Cottage cheese, low-fat	0.3g	73
Mascarpone	47.5g	460
Parmesan	25.8g	386
Emmental	30g	386
Shellfish	0.6g	77
Salmon	13.6g	202
Turkey breast (skinned)	1.0g	105
Turkey leg (skinned)	3.6g	114
Fillet steak	4.0g	121
Minced steak	14.0g	216
Pork fillet	2.0g	104
Pork chop	7.6g	150
Pork sausage	11.4g	169
Potatoes, boiled	0.1g	70
Chips	14.5g	290

Food for

eating and enjoying the right food

every day

MAKING SENSIBLE CHOICES

Using fat sparingly is the first step toward winning the battle against cellulite. But there is a lot more you can do when choosing your food and drink. We are lucky that nature provides us with a wide range of foods that can be very beneficial to our bodies, both generally and particularly in the battle against cellulite. For example, the silicic acid contained in some varieties of grain firms up the connective tissue, so that the fatty cells are less likely to become visible. Other substances stimulate the body's digestive system, and some aid in the efficient oxidation or burning of fat. The table opposite shows the effect these substances have on the body, together with some of the foods they are found in.

EVERY DAY

✱ Enjoy low-fat and carbohydrate-rich foods.
✱ Eat a lot of fruit, vegetables, and wholemeal products. Vitamins, minerals, and other ingredients firm up the connective tissue, encourage fat to be burned off, relieve water retention, and stimulate the metabolism.
✱ Feast on a wide variety of foods.

✱ Choose natural foods.
✱ Drink at least two litres (3 1/2 pints) of water each day, and avoid calorific drinks with a high sugar content, such as sugary fruit-juice drinks.
✱ Avoid salt. It leads to water retention.

NOT SO HELPFUL: EXPENSIVE CREAMS AND INJECTIONS

It is a real waste of money to buy so-called cellulite creams. The creams in themselves are not harmful, but they are also of dubious benefit. While it may be true that the action of rubbing the cream in does actually improve the blood supply to the skin, there is no lasting effect. The benefits of injections and more interventionist procedures are just as doubtful. In more severe cellulite cases, deposits of fat can be removed by suction, but unless this is accompanied by a change in diet, the deposits will soon build up again.

Any method will only help if you change your diet and take up a more active lifestyle. Unfortunately there is no miracle cure for cellulite.

Fighting cellulite from within

Substances contained in food	Effect on the body	Found in
Silicic acid	firms up the connective tissue, strengthens the skin	wholemeal cereals (especially millet, oats, barley)
Selenium	detoxifies, for beautiful skin	wholemeal cereals, nuts (especially Brazils), tuna, meat
Potassium	encourages kidney activity, reduces water retention	potatoes, bananas, cabbage, brown rice, fruits, cereals
Iron	for blood formation and blood supply, smooth skin	red meat, fish, millet, peas, beans, spinach, nuts, cabbage
Zinc	for healthy skin, healing spots	fish, meat, cereals, legumes, cheese, nuts, seaweed, oysters
Iodine	prevents thyroid deficiency	salt-water fish, iodized salt, seaweed
Vitamin E	preserves the connective tissue's elasticity, encourages blood supply	nutritious vegetable oils (especially wheat-germ oil, oily fish, cereals, nuts
Vitamin B_{12}	strengthens the connective tissue, important for cell division and blood formation	meat, milk products, eggs, fish, yeast extract, seaweed
Omega-3 fatty acids	promotes healthy blood supply	oily fish (herring, salmon), rapeseed and linseed oils
Gamma-linoleic acid	ensures healthy and firm skin	evening primrose oil, starflower oil
Secondary vegetable substances	helps protect against UV damage	fruit and vegetables
Bitter constituents	help with digestion, particularly of fats	broccoli, globe artichokes, legumes
Pungent constituents	stimulate digestion	spices such as ginger, chilli, pepper, paprika
Isothiocyanates	help with digestion, particularly of fats	cabbage, radishes, small root vegetables, onions, leeks

Body styling for
to make you fit, slim, and beautiful
a great figure

ESSENTIAL: EXERCISE

If you don't exercise, you don't just deteriorate physically, you also give cellulite an even greater chance. Do something about it: take up a sport. Sport builds up muscles while reducing your fatty padding. And it firms up the connective tissue, making the little fatty pockets much less, if at all, visible.

In the battle against cellulite, it makes most sense to take up a sport that demands stamina, such as cycling, swimming, walking, or jogging. It is more important, however, to find a sport that you also really enjoy, for otherwise you will probably give it up through boredom. Find someone who will exercise with you – it's more fun together, and increases motivation no end.

Make exercise an integral part of your day. Use the stairs instead of the lift. At the weekend, go walking in the woods or hills with family or friends, or go for a bike ride. Do your shopping on foot, cycle to the office, leave the car at home as often as possible, and go dancing again.

ANTI-CELLULITE EXERCISES

There are certain exercises that will help in the battle against unwanted dimples. But they must be the right ones, focused specifically on the problem areas, and you must do them regularly. Just ten minutes a day will put you well on the right track. Start on a moderate daily training programme.
✴ Don't over-exert yourself right at the start. If you build up your regime gradually, your body won't object. It will give you clear signals, whether you like it or not, if you are training too much, too often, or too quickly.
✴ This rule always applies: remember to breathe. Breathe out when tensing the muscles, and in when you relax.

For the exercises on the opposite page repeat each leg exercise at least twice and do two complete sets of exercises. Concentrate, and do the movements as slowly as possible; that way, they will be of greater value. Never use excessive movement in the exercises. In the leg exercises, the back should always be straight and the stomach stretched.

FOR THE OUTER THIGH

* Lie on your side on the floor, resting on your forearm. Support yourself on your other arm, with the palm of your hand parallel to your body.

* Raise your right leg as high as possible to the side, bending the foot slightly. Lower the leg again.

* Then change sides and repeat.

* This exercise can also be done standing. Support yourself with one hand against the wall for better balance. Both knees should always face forward.

* Cross the top leg over the leg below it, resting the foot in front of the thigh.

* Slowly raise and lower the straight leg, keeping it extended

FOR THE BUTTOCKS

* Lie flat on your back, always keeping your head on the floor. Place your arms alongside your body, then bend your legs.

* Raise your pelvis until your thighs and body form a straight line. Clench your buttocks and count to ten.

* Repeat twenty times. Then rest and repeat a further twenty times.

FOR THE INNER THIGH

* Lie on your side on the floor, resting on your forearm. Support yourself on your other arm, with the palm of your hand parallel to your body.

Power

Living it up to combat cellulite

week

GOODBYE ORANGE-PEEL SKIN

The best way to achieve success is to start your training programme straight away. Prepare and enjoy the recipes for the power week for seven days. Back up these culinary efforts with a little fitness programme (see pages 8–9). If you begin each day with at least ten minutes of exercises, go swimming or jogging, and don't use the car or the lift, you're sure to succeed. The pounds will melt away, your metabolism will speed up, and you will see a reduction in fat in all the critical places. This anti-cellulite programme will make you feel fit and healthy, without a hint of dieting or sacrifice.

THIS IS THE WEEK TO MAKE A FRESH START

Of course, you cannot expect miracles from just one healthy and active week – your orange-peel skin won't disappear overnight. But this power week will kick-start your battle against cellulite. Include as much of it as possible in your daily life. Tuck into the recommended foods with gusto. Prepare and eat low-fat foods, include exercise in your plan each day, and drink at least two litres (3 1/2 pints) each day: mainly water, herbal or fruit teas, and good fruit and vegetable juices diluted with water. But there's no reason why you can't enjoy the odd glass of wine or beer every now and again too.

THE PLAN FOR THE WEEK

Enjoy a carefully planned week. See our suggestions opposite for seven breakfasts, lunches, and evening meals. The recipes are quick and easy to prepare, and they are all included in this book. You can swap the individual days or recipes around as you think fit. If time is short, just make a delicious salad of crispy vegetables with a yoghurt dressing, or boil a few small potatoes and enjoy them with cottage cheese and herbs. Or bite into an apple, peel an orange, gulp down a carton of yoghurt, or fill a wholemeal roll with a little salad and low-fat cheese. There are all sorts of possibilities for a low-fat, low-calorie snack.

PLAN FOR THE WEEK

Monday

* Breakfast: fresh grain muesli with fruit yoghurt * Citrus drink with pink grapefruit
* Vegetable hotpot with polenta dumplings
* Potato boats with herbs * Fresh pineapple

Tuesday

* Breakfast: nut bread with cottage cheese and rocket * Fruity carrot cocktail
* Roast beef sandwich * Fresh fruit
* Stew with millet fritters * Blueberry sorbet

Wednesday

* Breakfast: pineapple and kiwi fruit salad, with a wholemeal bread roll and a glass
of buttermilk * Salad platter with chicken pieces, with a wholemeal bread roll
* Trout with red and green vegetables * Strawberries with vanilla yoghurt

Thursday

* Breakfast: fresh grain muesli with fruit yoghurt * Buttermilk with cranberries
* Stuffed vine leaves, with cucumber salad and yoghurt dressing
* Quick cabbage goulash * Berry custard

Friday

* Breakfast: wholemeal bread or bread roll with low-fat cheese, a glass of buttermilk
* Basil and tomato soup served with wholemeal bread
* Rock salmon and potato curry * Pineapple and coconut sorbet

Saturday

* Breakfast: orange and grapefruit muesli * Raspberry yoghurt shake
* Cucumber and lemon soup * Fresh pineapple
* Artichokes with a herb dip served with a wholemeal baguette * Caramelised apples

Sunday

* Smoked salmon with apples served with a wholemeal baguette * Mixed berry salad
* Oriental salad with squid * Fresh mango or kiwi fruit
* Poached fillet steak * Orange punch jelly

Pineapple

vitamin-rich to

and kiwi

raise your spirits

fruit salad

Serves two: • 2 kiwi fruits • 1/2 small pineapple • 100g (4 oz) black grapes

• 3 tbsp lime juice • 125g (5 oz) low-fat cottage cheese • 2 tbsp apple juice

• 3 tbsp chopped almonds

Peel the pineapple and remove its core, peel the kiwi fruits and chop the fruit into bite-size pieces. Wash, halve, and remove the seeds from the grapes. Place the fruits in a bowl and stir in 2 tablespoons of the lime juice. Mix the remaining lime juice with the cottage cheese and apple juice. Toast the almonds and combine with the cottage cheese, reserving a few for decoration. Add the cheese mixture to the fruit salad and sprinkle with the remaining almonds.

PER PORTION: 284 kcal • 13g protein • 9g fat • 40g carbohydrate

Mixed berry
burns off fat more quickly
salad

Serves two: • 100g (4 oz) each of red- and blackcurrants • 100g (4 oz) raspberries • 150g (6 oz) strawberries • 2 tbsp apple juice • 150g (6 oz) low-fat yoghurt • ground cinnamon • 4 tbsp rolled oats

Wash and drain the berries. Remove the stalks from the currants. Hull the raspberries and strawberries, then cut into halves or quarters. Mix the berries together. Combine the apple juice with the yoghurt and cinnamon, and arrange the berries on top. Toast the rolled oats in a non-stick frying pan and sprinkle over the fruit mixture.

PER PORTION: 233 kcal • 7g protein • 5g fat • 37g carbohydrate

Fresh grain muesli
soak the grain overnight
with fruit yoghurt

Serves two: • 75g (3 oz) freshly crushed spelt • 2 tbsp apple juice • 100g (4 oz) fresh fruit (e.g. berries) • 150g (6 oz) low-fat yoghurt • a few drops of vanilla essence

Combine the spelt in a bowl with 250ml (1/4 pt) water. Cover and leave in a cool place overnight. Stir the apple juice into the spelt. Wash and trim the fruits, cutting into small pieces if necessary. Mix some of the fruit with the yoghurt and vanilla essence. Arrange on plates with the spelt, topped with the remaining fruit.

PER PORTION: 207 kcal • 8g protein • 2g fat • 40g carbohydrate

Orange and
a perfect way to start your day
grapefruit muesli

Peel the oranges and grapefruits using a sharp knife. Separate the fruits into segments or cut out the individual slivers of fruit between the dividing skins, collecting the juice in a bowl.

Combine the mixed grain flakes with the wheatgerm and the linseeds, place in the middle of two deep plates, and arrange the fruit segments around.

Combine the yoghurt with the maple syrup and any fruit juice collected from the oranges and grapefruit. Pour over the grain mixture and sprinkle with the chopped pistachio nuts.

Serves two:

2 oranges

1 grapefruit

6 tbsp mixed grain flakes

3 tbsp wheatgerm

3 tbsp linseeds

200g (7 oz) low-fat yoghurt

2 tbsp maple syrup

2 tbsp chopped pistachio nuts

Citrus fruits

Citrus fruits are packed with the defensive vitamin C, but they are also a good source of beta-carotene, diuretic potassium, and other valuable constituents. Remove most of the pith, but remember that pith contains many flavonoids, which protect our cells – including the skin cells – against undesirable invaders and keep it looking young.

PER PORTION:

452 kcal

18g protein • 15g fat

60g carbohydrate

Nut bread with cottage

for a hearty start to the day

cheese and rocket

Toast the pine kernels in a non-stick frying pan without adding any fat.

Remove the stem, membranes, and seeds from the pepper, then wash,

drain, and cut into thin strips.

Serves two:
2 tbsp pine kernels
1/2 red or yellow pepper
a handful of rocket
200g (7 oz) cottage cheese
salt
black pepper
2 slices of wholemeal nut bread

Wash, shake dry, and trim the rocket, removing any

coarse stems. Chop coarsely and stir into the cottage

cheese, seasoning with salt and pepper.

Spread the slices of bread with the rocket and

cottage cheese mixture. Arrange the strips of pepper

on top and sprinkle with the pine kernels.

> ### Rocket – stimulating and invigorating

This popular salad leaf is a rich source of essential
oils and organic acids with an invigorating and
appetizing effect. Rocket stimulates the metabolism
and is an excellent purifier and diuretic, so it
definitely deserves a place on your plate more often.

PER PORTION:

228 kcal

18g protein • 10g fat

15g carbohydrate

power

Raspberry yoghurt shake

Drink to your own health

Serves two: • 125g (4 oz) raspberries • 2 tsps fruit juice • a few drops of vanilla essence • 250g (8 oz) low-fat yoghurt • 150ml (1/4 pt) mineral water (chilled)

Wash and hull the raspberries, then purée using a hand blender. If you wish, you can also pass the purée through a fine sieve to remove even the smallest seeds. Flavour the purée with the fruit juice and vanilla, stir in the yoghurt and mineral water, pour into two glasses, and serve immediately.

PER GLASS: 103 kcal • 5g protein • 2g fat • 11g carbohydrate

Buttermilk with cranberries

best served chilled

Serves two: • 125ml (5fl oz) cranberry juice • 2 tbsp pear juice • 1 tbsp rolled oats • 1/2 litre (9fl oz) buttermilk

Thoroughly combine the cranberry juice with the pear juice and rolled oats in a deep bowl. Add the buttermilk and mix well. Pour into two glasses and drink as soon as possible.

PER GLASS: 85 kcal • 3g protein • 1g fat • 18g carbohydrate

Citrus drink with

a daily power pack of vitamins

pink grapefruit

Serves two: • 1 lemon • 1 orange • 2 pink grapefruits • 2 tbsp sea buckthorn juice with honey (available from health food stores) • 1 tbsp wheatgerm

Squeeze the lemon, orange, and grapefruits, and pour the juice into a blender or deep mixing bowl. Add the sea buckthorn juice and wheatgerm, and combine all the ingredients thoroughly. Pour the drink into two glasses and enjoy immediately.

PER GLASS: 85 kcal • 3g protein • 1g fat • 16g carbohydrate

Fruity

vitamins straight from the juicer

carrot cocktail

Serves two: • 300g (11 oz) carrots • 2 pears • 1/2 lemon • 2 slices of pineapple • 1 tbsp pear juice • 1 tbsp wheatgerm • a few drops of vanilla essence

Wash and trim the carrots. Peel, quarter, and core the pears. Peel the lemon and the pineapple slices. Extract the juice from the carrots, pears, lemon, and pineapple in a juicer and immediately combine thoroughly with the pear juice, wheatgerm, and vanilla essence. Pour the cocktail into two glasses and serve immediately.

PER GLASS: 190 kcal • 3g protein • 1g fat • 42g carbohydrate

Smoked salmon
with valuable omega-3 fatty acids
with apple

Finely dice or chop the smoked salmon using a large sharp knife. Wash, dry, and core the apple. Dice finely and immediately sprinkle with the lemon juice. Add the smoked salmon, season with pepper, a little salt, and the coriander, and mix together carefully.

Combine the cream cheese and yoghurt, and spread over the slices of bread. Pile the salmon and apple mixture on the bread.

Wash the dill and shake dry, remove the leaves and scatter over the bread. Enjoy as soon as possible.

Serves two:
75g (3 oz) fresh smoked salmon
1 cooking apple
1 tbsp lemon juice
white pepper
salt
a pinch of ground coriander
2 tbsp full-fat cream cheese
2 tbsp natural yoghurt
2 slices of wholemeal bread
3 fronds of dill

▶ ### Salmon – a popular fish

This fish has a relatively high fat content, but it is an excellent source of omega-3 fatty acids, which the body cannot do without. These acids are involved in numerous metabolic processes, encourage the blood supply, and can help prevent heart and circulatory illnesses. Herring, mackerel, and tuna are also rich in omega-3 fatty acids.

PER PORTION:

266 kcal

15g protein • 13g fat

22g carbohydrate

Mini-pizzas
quick to make with frozen dough
with tuna

Leave the pizza dough to defrost under a tea towel. Grease a baking sheet.

Thinly roll out the pizza dough on a lightly floured worktop. Cut out disks

approximately 7cm (3 in) in diameter using a pastry

cutter or a glass and arrange them on the baking

sheet. Preheat the oven to 225°C (425°F).

Cut a cross in the tomato skin, blanch the tomatoes

in boiling water for a few seconds, remove from the

water, and peel. Remove the stalks. Cut the tomatoes

into quarters, remove the seeds, dice finely, and

arrange on the mini-pizzas.

Wash and shake dry the basil. Pick off the leaves and

cut them into very fine strips. Sprinkle over the mini-

pizzas and season with salt and pepper.

Peel and finely dice the shallots. Drain the tuna and

fork into small pieces. Sprinkle both over the mini-pizzas. Drain

the mozzarella, then chop it into small pieces and sprinkle over

the mini-pizzas. Bake the mini-pizzas on a low shelf in the oven

for about 15 minutes.

Makes 12:
frozen pizza dough
(approx. 150g/6 oz)
oil for the baking sheet
flour for rolling
2 tomatoes
4 sprigs of basil
salt
black pepper
1 shallot
1 small tin tuna in spring water
(80g/3 oz net; 65g/2 oz when
drained)
80g (3 oz) mozzarella cheese

PER MINI-PIZZA: 60 kcal • 3g protein • 2g fat • 7g carbohydrate

Crostini with

best served as a starter

prawns

Serves two:

100g (4 oz) peeled cooked
prawns

1 tbsp lemon juice

2 sprigs of flat-leaf parsley

chives

2 tbsp ricotta cheese

salt

white pepper

a handful of rocket

4–6 small slices of wholemeal
bread

1 clove of garlic

Place the prawns in a sieve and run under cold water. Drain well, transfer to a bowl, and drizzle with the lemon juice. Wash and shake dry the parsley and chives, then chop finely or roll up and slice finely. Reserve some parsley and chives for the garnish. Mix the remaining herbs with the ricotta, and add to the prawns. Season lightly with salt and pepper and combine carefully. Wash, shake dry, and trim the rocket, removing any coarse stems. Chop or tear the leaves into smaller pieces if necessary.

Toast the slices of bread. Peel and halve the garlic clove, and rub over the slices of bread. Arrange the rocket and the prawn and ricotta mixture on top. Serve sprinkled with parsley or chives.

Wholemeal bread

Eat more wholemeal bread and less white bread. Wholemeal grain contains substances that prevent cellulite: silicic acid for example, which strengthens the connective tissue and the skin; selenium, which detoxifies the body and helps achieve beautiful skin; and potassium, a diuretic, and therefore good for firming up the problem areas.

PER PORTION:

247 kcal

18g protein • 6g fat

31g carbohydrate

power

Roast beef

a classic quick and easy light lunch

sandwich

Peel and crush the garlic, then combine with the cottage cheese, salt, pepper, and herbs. Season generously. Drain the pickled gherkins and slice into long, thin strips. Wash and dry the tomatoes, remove the stalks, then slice. Wash and shake dry the lettuce, tearing it into smaller pieces if necessary. Toast the bread and spread with the cottage cheese mixture. Stack 3 slices of spread toast one on top of the other, placing the lettuce, gherkin and tomato slices, and roast beef between them. Place the remaining slices of toast on top, press the sandwiches together, and cut in half diagonally.

Serves 2:

1 small clove of garlic

100g (4 oz) low-fat cottage cheese

salt

black pepper

1 tbsp chopped mixed herbs

4 pickled gherkins

2 tomatoes

2 lettuce leaves

6 thin slices of wholemeal bread

6 thin slices of cold roast beef (about 100g/4 oz)

Herbs

Every meal should include some tender, green leaves, not just because they taste good, but also because they are good for your health. Herbs are packed with valuable constituents. They stimulate the appetite and digestion, and help purify the body.

PER PORTION:

275 kcal

25g protein • 5g fat

34g carbohydrate

Vegetable sushi rolls

Japanese finger food

Serves two:
125g (4 oz) Japanese sticky rice
1 tbsp rice vinegar
1 tsp sugar
salt
1 egg
cucumber
a small piece of black radish
a few endive leaves
**5 leaves of dried seaweed
(*nori*, available at Oriental
food stores)**
**1–2 tsp green horseradish
(*wasabi*, available at Oriental
food stores)**
5–6 tbsp soy sauce

Rinse the rice in a sieve and leave to drain. Place in a pan and bring to the boil with barely 200ml (7fl oz) water. Cover tightly and leave the rice to swell over a low heat for about 20 minutes, then combine immediately with the rice vinegar, sugar, and a little salt. Cover and leave to cool.

Beat the egg with a little salt and use to make a thin omelette in a small, non-stick frying pan over a low heat. Cut the omelette into thin strips. Wash and peel the cucumber and black radish, then cut into long, thin strips. Wash, dry, and shred the endive leaves.

Using scissors, cut the nori leaves into quarters. Place a little rice, a few omelette strips, some cucumber, black radish, lettuce, and a little wasabi on each piece, and roll it up to form a cone. Serve with soy sauce as a dip.

PER PORTION: 303 kcal • 11g protein • 4g fat • 57g carbohydrate

Potato boats

a potassium-rich nibble for the cocktail hour

with herbs

Wash and scrub the potatoes thoroughly. Put into a pan of slightly salted water, cover, and cook for barely 20 minutes until just soft.

Serves 2:
400g (14 oz) small new potatoes
salt
3 tender spring onions
1/2 bunch flat-leaf parsley
a few sprigs of thyme
3 tbsp cream
black pepper
cayenne pepper
60g (2 oz) grated Emmental cheese

Preheat the oven to 225°C (425°F). Trim and wash the spring onions, then slice into very thin rings. Wash, dry, and chop the parsley and thyme. Stir the spring onions, parsley, and chives into the cream, and season with black pepper and cayenne pepper. Drain the potatoes and leave to cool slightly, then cut them in half. Hollow out slightly using a teaspoon, and fill with the herb mixture. Place the potatoes in an ovenproof dish, sprinkle with the cheese, and bake on the middle shelf of the oven for 10 minutes.

Potatoes

Contrary to popular opinion, these delicious tubers will not make you fat. Potatoes can help anyone attain a slim waistline provided they are not eaten as chips or crisps. They are good diuretics and thus firm up the skin.

PER PORTION:

285 kcal

13g protein • 13g fat

28g carbohydrate

power

Stuffed
a popular Greek snack
vine leaves

Bring about 150ml (5fl oz) salted water to the boil. Add the rice, cover, and cook over a low heat for 20–40 minutes (depending on the variety) until al dente, adding a little water if necessary.

Wash and drain the raisins, then leave to marinate in the lemon juice in a small bowl. Crumble the feta.

Wash, shake dry, and finely chop the parsley.

Transfer the cooked rice to a bowl and stir in the raisins, feta, and parsley. Season with salt and pepper.

Rinse the vine leaves under cold water. Spread them out on kitchen paper, place 1/2 tablespoon of the rice mixture on each leaf and then wrap them up, folding the sides of the leaves inward.

Serves two:

60g (2 oz) brown rice

3 tbsp raisins

1 tbsp lemon juice

30g (1 oz) feta cheese

3 sprigs of flat-leaf parsley

salt

black pepper

12 preserved vine leaves (about 85g/3 oz)

1 tbsp olive oil

200ml (7fl oz) vegetable stock

Arrange the vine leaf parcels tightly together in a small pan. Add the oil and stock, cover, and leave the parcels to cook over a low heat for about 30 minutes. Delicious served warm or cold.

PER PORTION: 233 kcal • 5g protein • 9g fat • 33g carbohydrate

Oriental salad
with spicy ginger
with squid

Wash the squid and pat dry with kitchen paper. Peel and finely dice the ginger and garlic. In a bowl, mix together 1 1/2 tablespoons soya oil and some pepper. Add the squid to this mixture.

To make the dressing, combine the remaining soya oil with 2 tablespoons of soy sauce, the rice vinegar, sambal oelek, and sesame oil. Trim and wash the Chinese leaves, then cut into fine strips. Run the bean sprouts under cold water and leave to drain thoroughly in a sieve. Toss the Chinese leaves and bean sprouts well in the dressing and arrange on two plates.

Heat a non-stick frying pan and fry the squid for about 5 minutes, turning occasionally. Season the squid with the remaining soy sauce and serve on the bed of salad.

Serves two:

350g (12 oz) squid cut into rings (ready-prepared)

30g (1 oz) root ginger

1 clove of garlic

3 tbsp soya oil

black pepper

4 tbsp light soy sauce

2 tbsp rice vinegar

1/4 tsp *sambal oelek* (available from Oriental food stores)

1 tsp sesame oil

1 small bunch Chinese leaves (about 400g/14 oz)

100g (4 oz) fresh bean sprouts

PER PORTION: 386 kcal • 34g protein • 22g fat • 13g carbohydrate

Colourful rice
with lots of fresh vegetables
noodle stir fry

Leave the noodles to soften in plenty of warm water for about 20 minutes.
Trim and wash the celery and red pepper. Slice the celery and cut the

Serves two:
125g (5 oz) thick rice noodles
4 sticks celery
1 red pepper
1 clove of garlic
20g (1 oz) root ginger
1 tbsp oil
1 small tin of sweetcorn (about 150g/6 oz)
1 tsp *sambal oelek* (available from Oriental food stores)
3 tbsp light soy sauce
salt
black pepper

pepper into strips. Peel the garlic and ginger and dice finely.

Heat the oil in a wok or large frying pan. Quickly fry the garlic and ginger, stirring constantly. Add the celery and red pepper and fry for about 3 minutes. Drain the noodles. Add the sweetcorn and the noodles to the vegetables and fry briefly. Season with sambal oelek and soy sauce and heat thoroughly. Season with salt and black pepper.

Celery and celeriac

Both celery and celeriac are tasty vegetables that help to get rid of excess water from the body and stimulate the metabolism and digestion. They are particularly good at getting fat digestion going, which is why celery is also regarded as a fat burner.

PER PORTION:

566 kcal

18g protein • 9g fat

103g carbohydrate

Spring vegetable
with fat-burning asparagus and chervil
ragout with salmon

Wash and trim the asparagus, then peel the bottom third. Cut into 3 cm (1 1/2 in) long pieces. Trim and peel the carrots and kohlrabi, then cut into pieces the same size as the asparagus.

Gently heat the olive oil in a pan, sprinkle the flour over, and stir in. Gradually whisk in the vegetable stock. Bring the sauce to the boil, stirring constantly. Add the vegetables, cover, and leave to simmer over a low heat for about 10 minutes.

Rinse the salmon fillet in cold water and pat dry. Cut into strips and season with the lemon juice, salt, and pepper. Add the salmon strips to the vegetables, cover, and cook over a low heat for 5 minutes. Wash, shake dry, and shred the chervil, then add to the ragout. Season with salt and pepper.

Serves two:

500g (1 lb) asparagus

2 carrots

2 small kohlrabi

1 tbsp olive oil

2 tsp wheat flour

1/4 litre (9fl oz) vegetable stock

175g (6 oz) salmon fillet

2 tbsp lemon juice

salt

white pepper

a handful of chervil

PER PORTION: 342 kcal • 25g protein • 18g fat • 19g carbohydrate

to nibble at

Fruity
turkey kebabs

Rinse the turkey breast in cold water, pat dry, and cut into small cubes. Combine the soy sauce, pepper, and Chinese five-spice powder in a small bowl, and then toss the turkey pieces in this mixture.

Serves two:
150g (6 oz) turkey breast
2 tbsp soy sauce
black pepper
a little Chinese five-spice
powder
1 tbsp oil
2 thin slices fresh pineapple
80g (3 oz) black seedless
grapes
2–3 lettuce leaves
20 small wooden kebab sticks

Brush the oil over the surface of a non-stick frying pan and heat. Fry the marinated turkey over a moderate heat for about 5 minutes, turning repeatedly, until golden brown. Remove the meat from the frying pan and leave to cool slightly.

Meanwhile, peel the pineapple slices, remove the cores, and cut the remaining flesh into chunks. Wash and drain the grapes. Wash the lettuce thoroughly, shake dry, and shred into small pieces. Push the meat, fruits, and lettuce on to the kebab sticks and serve.

➤ **Almost fat-free frying**

Even if you are using a non-stick frying pan, you will have to add a little fat if food is not to stick. But here's a simple trick to keep the amount of fat required to a minimum: use a brush to spread the oil over the frying pan prior to heating. This way the pan will be completely covered with a very thin film of oil.

PER PORTION:

167 kcal

19g protein • 6g fat

11g carbohydrate

Vegetable hotpot with
a fine Italian speciality
polenta dumplings

Serves two: • 500g (1 lb 2 oz) vegetables (e.g. broccoli, celery, fennel, onions, carrots)
• 800ml (1 1/2 pints) vegetable stock • 6–7 tbsp polenta • salt • pepper • 2 tbsp grated Parmesan

Wash, scrub, and dice the vegetables. Bring 600ml (1 pint) stock to the boil. Add the vegetables, cover and simmer for about 15 minutes. Bring the remaining stock to the boil in another pan, stir in the polenta, and cook until thickened. Season with salt and pepper. Using a tablespoon, shape the polenta into dumplings. Pour the vegetable soup over the dumplings and sprinkle with grated Parmesan.

PER PORTION: 223 kcal • 11g protein • 4g fat • 35g carbohydrate

Cucumber and
to cleanse the body
lemon soup

Serves two: • 1/2 litre (18 fl oz) vegetable stock • 60g (2 oz) brown rice • a small cucumber • zest and juice of 1 small, unwaxed lemon • 100g (4 oz) natural yoghurt • salt • white pepper • a few mint leaves

Cook the rice in the stock according to the instructions on the packet. Peel the cucumber and grate coarsely. Mix the lemon zest and some of the juice with the yoghurt, salt, and pepper. Add the grated cucumber and the remaining lemon juice to the soup and season to taste. Stir in yoghurt and chopped mint leaves, and serve.

PER PORTION: 206 kcal • 5g protein • 5g fat • 35g carbohydrate

Basil and

thickened with potatoes for a low calorie dish

tomato soup

Peel, wash, and coarsely dice the potatoes. Add to the stock and bring to the boil.
Cover and cook over a low heat for about 20 minutes.

Wash the basil and shake dry . Tear off and finely chop the
leaves, reserving a few whole ones for the garnish.

Liquidise the potatoes and stock in a blender to form a smooth
purée. Return to the pan and bring back to the boil. Stir in the
chopped basil and the cream, and season the soup with salt and
pepper. Wash and quarter the tomatoes, remove the stalks and
seeds, and cut into small pieces. Sprinkle the diced tomato over
the soup and serve with a garnish of basil leaves.

Serves two:
300g (10 oz) floury potatoes
400ml (14fl oz) vegetable stock
1 bunch fresh basil
2 tbsp cream
salt
white pepper
2 small, firm tomatoes

Cream soups the healthy way

Sadly, if cream soups are made with lots
of butter, flour, or cream, they are
extremely high in fatty calories. But
there is a healthier way: cook potatoes in
with the soup and then blend it, for
potatoes are a wonderfully low-calorie
way of thickening soup perfectly. What's
more, they will give you an extra dose of
that important mineral, potassium.

PER PORTION:

154 kcal

3g protein • 4g fat

23g carbohydrate

Salad platter with
chicken pieces
with a refreshing yoghurt dressing

Peel one orange and divide into segments, collecting any juice. Squeeze the second orange and combine the juice with the cider vinegar, yoghurt, and walnut oil until smooth, then season with salt, pepper, and coriander.

Rinse the chicken breast in cold water, pat dry, and cut into bite-size pieces. Season with salt, pepper, and coriander. Grill for 3–4 minutes each side. Meanwhile, wash the chicory, remove the outer leaves and stalk, and separate the individual leaves. Wash the lamb's lettuce, pat dry, and shred. Arrange the chicory and lamb's lettuce on two plates and drizzle the dressing over them. Top with the orange segments and chicken pieces and sprinkle with chopped walnuts.

Serves two:

2 oranges

1 tbsp cider vinegar

100g (4 oz) low-fat yoghurt (1.5% fat)

2 tsp walnut oil

salt

white pepper

ground coriander

200g (7 oz) chicken breast

1 head of chicory

a handful of lamb's lettuce

2 tbsp chopped walnuts

power

PER PORTION: 272 kcal • 27g protein • 9g fat • 22g carbohydrate

Artichokes with

a slow-cooked dish for gourmets

a herb dip

Put a few slices of lemon in a large pan of salted water and bring to the boil. Snap off the artichoke stalks. Using scissors, cut off the upper third of the pointed leaves. Put the artichokes into the boiling lemon-flavoured water and cook over a moderate heat for about 40 minutes. They are cooked when the leaves can be pulled off easily.

Meanwhile, prepare the dip. Wash, shake dry, and finely chop the herbs. Combine with the cider vinegar, yoghurt, and cream, then season with salt and pepper.

Lift the artichokes out of the water and leave to drain. Place on two plates and serve with the dip. To eat, use your fingers to pluck out an artichoke leaf, dip the lower, fleshy end in the dip, and squeeze out the flesh from the leaves with your teeth. When all the leaves have been removed, remove the unappetizing "choke" to reveal the juicy, aromatic "heart".

Serves two:
salt
1 small untreated lemon
2 artichokes (about 500g/1 lb each)
mixed fresh herbs
1 tsp cider vinegar
100g (4 oz) low-fat yoghurt
2 tbsp cream
white pepper

Healthy artichokes

The cynarin contained in artichokes stimulates the liver and gall bladder and encourages the blood supply to these organs, as well as helping to digest fats and reduce water retention.

PER PORTION:

101 kcal

8g protein • 3g fat

12g carbohydrate

Tagliatelle
an extremely sophisticated purifier
with asparagus

Wash and trim the asparagus, then peel the lower third. Cut the asparagus into bite-size pieces. Wash and trim the dandelion leaves or rocket, then cut into broad strips. Coarsely chop the walnuts. Peel and finely chop the shallots.

Bring a large quantity of salted water to the boil in a pan. Cook the tagliatelle according to the instructions on the packet, until al dente. Meanwhile, bring some water to the boil in a second pan, then add salt, a pinch of sugar, and 1 teaspoon butter. Add the asparagus and cook for about 5 minutes until al dente. Remove from the heat and drain.

Brush the walnut oil over a non-stick frying pan and heat. Add the shallots and cook until translucent. Add the dandelion leaves or rocket, followed by the asparagus and tagliatelle. Combine thoroughly. Season with salt and pepper. Sprinkle with the walnuts and cheese and serve immediately.

Serves two:
500g (1 lb) asparagus
a handful of dandelion leaves or rocket
2 tbsp walnuts
2 shallots
200g (7 oz) tagliatelle
a pinch of sugar
1 tsp butter
1 tbsp walnut oil
salt
white pepper
2 tbsp grated cheese

PER PORTION: 521 kcal • 20g protein • 12g fat • 84g carbohydrate

Lentil and vegetable
and an apple surprise
salad with prawns

Wash the prawns and pat dry. Peel and finely chop the garlic and ginger. Combine the salt, cayenne pepper, and 2 tablespoons of lemon juice. Toss the prawns in this mixture.

Trim and wash the spring onions, then slice diagonally. Peel, quarter, and core the apples. Chop the quarters across to form reasonably thick chunks and immediately drizzle over the remaining lemon juice.

Bring the vegetable stock to the boil. Add the lentils and the white parts of the spring onions, cover, and cook over a low heat for about 5 minutes. Then add the apple chunks and the green parts of the spring onions and cook for a further 3 minutes. Season with salt, pepper, and cumin.

Brush the oil over the surface of a non-stick frying pan and heat. Fry the prawns for about 4 minutes, then arrange with the lentil and vegetable mixture on two plates. Sprinkle with the washed, dried, and shredded coriander leaves.

Serves two:
8–10 king prawns
1 clove of garlic
a small piece of root ginger
4 tbsp lemon juice
salt
cayenne pepper
1 bunch spring onions
2 small cooking apples
200ml (7fl oz) vegetable stock
100g (4 oz) red lentils
ground cumin
1 tbsp oil
a few coriander leaves

PER PORTION: 366 kcal • 29g protein • 9g fat • 41g carbohydrate

Trout with red

cooked in a roasting bag

and green vegetables

Preheat the oven to 200°C (400°F). Wash the trout, pat dry, then season with lemon juice, salt, and pepper. Place in a roasting bag.

Serves two:

2 fresh trout (prepared weight about 300g/10 oz each)

2 tbsp lemon juice

salt

white pepper

2 small carrots

1 small onion

1 small fennel bulb

150ml (5fl oz) fish stock

Peel the carrots and onions. Trim the fennel. Finely dice them all, mix them together with the fish stock and pour into the roasting bag with the trout. Seal the bag with a tie.

Place the roasting bag on a baking sheet and prick the top a few times with a needle. Bake the trout for about 20 minutes on a low shelf in the oven. Open the bag and carefully transfer the vegetables, juices, and trout on to two plates and serve immediately.

Roasting bags

Why isn't cooking in a roasting bag more popular? You don't need to use a drop of fat, and the food turns out wonderfully light. What's more, all the vitamins, minerals, and aromas are retained and do not disappear into thin air. If roasting bags are not available, use aluminium foil instead. Cut two sufficiently long pieces of foil, place the trout on one sheet, and spread with the vegetables and stock. Cover with the other piece of foil , then fold and seal both ends.

PER PORTION:

356 kcal

61g protein • 9g fat

7g carbohydrate

Rock salmon and
wonderfully fresh and spicy
potato curry

Wash and peel the potatoes, then cut into bite-size pieces. Brush the oil over the surface of a small, non-stick frying pan and heat. Fry the potatoes over a moderate heat for about 20 minutes, stirring frequently.

Meanwhile, blanch, peel, and finely dice the tomatoes. Wash and trim the spring onions, then slice into fine rings. Peel and chop the garlic and root ginger.

Rinse the rock salmon in cold water, pat dry, and cut into bite-size pieces. Season with salt, black pepper, and lemon juice.

Add the spring onions, garlic, and ginger to the potatoes and brown quickly.

Stir the flour and garam masala into the yoghurt, then combine with the potatoes. Add the rock salmon and tomatoes, folding them in gently. Season the curry with salt and pepper, and cook over a low heat for at least 5 minutes.

Serves two:
400g (14 oz) waxy potatoes
1 tbsp oil
2 tomatoes
2 spring onions
1 clove of garlic
20g (1 oz) root ginger
200g (7 oz) rock salmon fillet
salt
black pepper
2 tbsp lemon juice
100g (4 oz) low-fat yoghurt
1/2 tsp flour
1/2–1 tbsp garam masala

PER PORTION: 272 kcal • 24g protein • 6g fat • 29g carbohydrate

Poached
with plenty of garlic
fillet steak

Serves two:
2 tender leeks
1 carrot
1 stick of celery
300g (10 oz) fillet steak
salt
black pepper
ground coriander
1/2 litre (18fl oz) beef stock
2–3 tbsp semolina
1 tbsp cream

Trim the leeks, slit lengthways, wash, and cut into rings. Peel the carrot and celery, then cut into fine strips. Rinse the steak in cold water and pat dry with kitchen paper, cut into slices about 1/2cm (1/4 in) thick and rub in the pepper and coriander.

Bring the beef stock to the boil. Add the vegetables and cook for about 5 minutes. Reduce the heat, add the meat to the vegetables, cover, and poach over a low heat for about 2 minutes.

Keep the meat warm by putting it in a bowl with one third of the stock. Add salt to the vegetables, stir in the semolina and cream, and return to the boil. Arrange on two plates with the meat and serve.

Leeks – an anti-cellulite vegetable

Leeks are a rich source of vitamin C, iron, magnesium, and calcium – all of which help to digest fat. Leeks also contain isothiocyanates, which stimulate the digestion and reduce water retention.

PER PORTION:

280 kcal

36g protein • 8g fat

15g carbohydrate

Stew with

a rich source of silicic acid

millet fritters

Serves two:
75g (3 oz) millet
400ml (14fl oz) vegetable stock
350g (12 oz) broccoli
3 tbsp chopped parsley
2 small eggs
2 tbsp olive oil
250g (8 oz) turkey breast
2 tsp wholemeal flour salt
white pepper
ground cumin

Place the millet in a pan with 200ml (7fl oz) stock and bring to the boil. Cover and cook over a low heat for 20 minutes, then leave to cool slightly. Wash and trim the broccoli, divide into small rosettes, and peel the stalks. Place in a pan of lightly salted water, cover, and cook for 5–6 minutes until al dente.

Combine the cooked millet with the parsley and beaten eggs. Brush the surface of a wide, non-stick frying pan with a tablespoon of olive oil, then heat. Shape the millet mixture into 8 small fritters, then fry over a low to moderate heat. Meanwhile, chop the meat. Heat the remaining olive oil in a second frying pan and brown the meat rapidly. Sprinkle with flour, then add the remaining stock, stirring constantly. Add the broccoli and season with salt, pepper, and cumin. Serve with the fritters.

Millet

Millet has the highest mineral content of all grains and is therefore exceptionally rich in silicic acid, which firms up the connective tissue and prevents cellulite. These small, round grains have other advantages too: they are quick to cook, very versatile, and easy to digest.

PER PORTION:

532 kcal

46g protein • 21g fat

37g carbohydrate

Quick
strengthens and firms up the connective tissue
cabbage goulash

Halve the peppers, then remove the stalks, white membranes, and seeds.

Wash the pepper halves, shake dry, and cut into thin strips.

Rinse the pork fillet in cold water, pat dry with kitchen paper, then cut into bite-size pieces. Heat the oil in a pan. Add the meat and brown quickly over a high heat. Season with salt, pepper, and paprika. Add the pickled cabbage, the pepper strips and the caraway. Mix well, cover, and simmer over a low heat for about 15 minutes. Adjust the seasoning. Sprinkle with chives and serve with a dollop of soured cream.

Serves two:

1 red pepper

1 green pepper

200g (7 oz) pork fillet

1 tbsp oil

salt

black pepper

paprika

1 small tin pickled cabbage (300g/10 oz)

1/2–1 tsp caraway (ground if possible)

2 tbsp soured cream

1–2 tbsp chopped chives

Pickled cabbage

Cabbage is a versatile source of many vital substances and is excellent in the battle against cellulite. Vitamin B_{12} strengthens the connective tissue, potassium is a diuretic, and iron ensures a good blood supply – including to the skin in the problem areas.

PER PORTION:

218 kcal

25g protein • 7g fat

11 g carbohydrate

Sweet and sour chicken

serve with brown rice

Peel the ginger and garlic and dice finely. Combine with the soy sauce, rice vinegar, and Chinese five-spice powder to make a marinade.

Rinse the chicken breast in cold water, pat dry, then chop into small pieces, and place in the marinade. Cover and leave in a cool place for at least 30 minutes.

Wash and trim the spring onions, then cut diagonally into thin rings. Peel the carrots and cut into julienne strips. Peel the pineapple slices, remove the hard cores, and cut into chunks.

Brush the oil over the surface of a non-stick frying pan, then heat. Remove the meat from the marinade and brown quickly in the frying pan, together with the vegetables.

Stir the stock, tomato purée, and cornflour into the marinade, pour into the frying pan, and bring to the boil. Stir in the pineapple pieces, season with the salt, pepper, and sugar, and simmer for 2–3 minutes.

Serves two:
20g (1 oz) root ginger
1 clove of garlic
4 tbsp light soy sauce
2 tbsp rice vinegar
1/2 tsp Chinese five-spice powder
200g (7 oz) chicken breast
1 bunch spring onions
2 carrots
3 slices fresh pineapple
2 tsp oil
200ml (7fl oz) chicken stock
2 tbsp tomato purée
1 tsp cornflour
salt
pepper
sugar

PER PORTION: 434 kcal • 37g protein • 12g fat • 47g carbohydrate

Orange punch jelly

a light, warming winter dessert

Put the fruit tea in a teapot and pour on 1/4 litre (9fl oz) boiling water. Add the cinnamon stick, cloves, and star anise, and leave the tea to infuse for about 10 minutes.

Soften the gelatine in plenty of hot water. Rinse the oranges in hot water, then dry. Finely grate some of the zest and squeeze the juice of one orange. Peel the remaining orange, then divide into segments, collecting the juice.

Strain the fruit tea through a fine sieve. Gently squeeze the gelatine to remove excess water and dissolve in the hot tea. Stir the orange peel, orange juice, and apple juice into the tea.

Arrange the orange segments in star shapes in two deep dishes or glasses. Carefully add the tea and leave to set in a refrigerator. Decorate with the mint leaves. Beat the vanilla sugar and cream together until smooth and serve with the punch jelly.

Serves two:
- 2 tbsp loose winter-fruits tea
- 1/2 cinnamon stick
- 2 cloves
- 1 star anise
- 4 leaves white gelatine
- 2 oranges
- 2 tbsp apple juice
- 2 tbsp cream
- 2 tsp vanilla sugar
- 2–4 mint leaves

PER PORTION: 139 kcal • 5g protein • 3g fat • 26g carbohydrate

Caramelised

for dessert or as a snack

apples

Serves two: • 2 cooking apples • 2 tbsp lemon juice • 2 tsp butter • 1 tsp honey • 2 tsp cream • 2 tsp chopped pistachio nuts

Peel, quarter, and core the apples. Cut the quarters in half and toss immediately in the lemon juice. In a small pan, melt the butter and honey over a moderate heat. Add the apple chunks and cook for 2–5 minutes until just soft. Put the apples, with their juice, on to plates, drizzle with the cream, and sprinkle with the pistachio nuts.

PER PORTION: 137 kcal • 1g protein • 5g fat • 22g carbohydrate

Blueberry

it couldn't be quicker

sorbet

Serves two: • 150g (6 oz) frozen blueberries • 2 tbsp icing sugar • 2 tbsp lemon juice • 1 tbsp fruit schnapps (optional)

Blend the still-frozen blueberries with the icing sugar, lemon juice, and fruit schnapps (if using) to form a creamy sorbet. Serve immediately.

PER PORTION: 111 kcal • 1g protein • 1g fat • 23g carbohydrate

Pineapple and

a natural slimming agent

coconut sorbet

Put the sugar and 6 tablespoons of water in a small pan. Bring to the boil and leave the sugar to melt. Dissolve the coconut powder in the sugar water and leave the syrup to cool.

Rinse the limes in hot water, dry, then grate the rind finely and squeeze the juice. Stir the zest and juice into the syrup. Place in a bowl in the freezer, and leave to freeze for about 3 hours, stirring frequently. Cut the pineapple into thin slices, then peel, and remove the hard core. Cut the slices in half and arrange on plates. Blend the coconut sorbet thoroughly in a blender and spoon over the pineapple pieces. Roast the desiccated coconut in a dry frying pan and sprinkle over the pineapple and coconut sorbet.

Serves two:

3 tbsp sugar

3 tbsp unsweetened coconut powder (from Oriental food stores)

2 limes

1/2 small pineapple

2 tbsp desiccated coconut

Pineapple

This "queen of fruits" is a rich source of iron, iodine, potassium, magnesium, and zinc – all minerals that have a beneficial effect on fat digestion. Pineapple is also a diuretic and purifier. It contains bromelin, an enzyme that is excellent at breaking down protein, making it easier to digest.

PER PORTION:

280 kcal

2g protein • 16g fat

30g carbohydrate

Buttermilk jelly

best prepared in advance

Soften the gelatine in plenty of cold water. Rinse the lemon in hot water, then dry. Cut some of the rind into fine strips and finely grate the remainder.

Serves two:
3 leaves white gelatine
Rind and juice of 1 unwaxed lemon
250g (9 oz) buttermilk
3 tbsp pear juice
1 ripe pear
a few mint leaves

Place the wet gelatine in a cup of hot water and leave to dissolve, then whisk into the buttermilk drop by drop. Fold in the lemon zest, half of the lemon juice, and 2 tablespoons of pear juice. Pour into two deep moulds (each with a capacity of about 150ml/5fl oz) and leave to set.

Peel, quarter, and core the pear, then cut into chunks, or slice the pear thinly as shown on the opposite page. Place immediately in a small pan together with the remaining lemon juice and the pear juice. Cover and simmer for 1/2–1 minute, then leave to cool in the juice. Turn out the buttermilk jelly on to plates, arrange the pear around it, and serve decorated with strips of lemon rind and whole mint leaves.

Thirst quencher and fat burner in one

Buttermilk is a soured milk product and has a beneficial effect on the digestion. This healthy thirst quencher is also very low in fat and calories, making it an excellent choice for delicate desserts and cakes.

PER PORTION:

158 kcal

7g protein • 1g fat

32g carbohydrate

Strawberries with
ideally eat one a day
vanilla yoghurt

Serves two: • 300g (10 oz) strawberries • 1 tbsp sugar • 200g (7 oz) yoghurt • 1 tbsp cream cheese

• 2 tsp clear honey • 1/4 tsp vanilla essence • a few lemon balm leaves

Wash, drain, and hull the strawberries. Halve or quarter the fruits, then sprinkle with the sugar. Combine the yoghurt, cream cheese, honey, and vanilla essence. Arrange the strawberries on two plates and spoon over the yoghurt mixture. Wash the lemon balm leaves, pat dry, and use to decorate the dessert.

PER PORTION: 150 kcal • 5g protein • 5g fat • 20g carbohydrate

Berry
simple and low in calories
custard

Serves two: • 2 eggs, separated • 1 tbsp vanilla sugar • 1 tbsp ground almonds • 125g (5 oz) cottage cheese • 200g (7 oz) mixed berries (strawberries, raspberries, blueberries, redcurrants) • butter

Preheat the oven to 200°C (400°F). Beat the egg whites until stiff. Mix the egg yolks, vanilla sugar, almonds, and cottage cheese until smooth. Carefully fold in the beaten egg whites. Wash and prepare the berries. Butter a shallow dish and pour in the egg mixture, then add the berries. Bake on the middle shelf of the oven for about 25 minutes.

PER PORTION: 239 kcal • 17g protein • 13g fat • 14g carbohydrate

Redcurrant and
served with wine mousse
raspberry fruit salad

Wash the raspberries and redcurrants, then leave to drain thoroughly. Hull the raspberries and carefully remove the redcurrant stalks. Mix the berries with the vanilla sugar, cover, and leave to steep in a refrigerator for about 30 minutes.

Combine the egg yolk with the icing sugar in a bowl. Bring a little water to the boil in a small pan, then reduce the heat so that the water is just simmering gently. Place the bowl containing the egg yolk on top and using a hand whisk beat the egg yolk until creamy. Gradually add the Marsala, and beat until the mixture is thick and frothy. Arrange the cream and fruits on two plates and serve decorated with lemon balm leaves.

Serves two:
150g (6 oz) raspberries
150g (6 oz) redcurrants
1 tsp vanilla sugar
1 small egg yolk
1 tbsp icing sugar
4 tbsp dry Marsala wine
lemon balm leaves

Berries – not just good to look at

All berries – strawberries, raspberries, blueberries, or redcurrants – are a great help in the battle against cellulite. They contain vitamin C, which not only protects against infections, but also helps the body to burn off fat. Other constituents strengthen the connective tissue, reduce water retention, and stimulate the metabolism. So you should eat berry fruits as often as possible.

PER PORTION:

113 kcal

3g protein • 3g fat

15g carbohydrate

power

Index

Anti-cellulite recipes

> **Abbreviations**
> tsp = teaspoon
> tbsp = tablespoon
> kcal = kilocalories

Imprint

First published in the UK by
Gaia Books Ltd, 20 High Street,
Stroud, GL5 1AZ
www.gaiabooks.co.uk

Registered at 66 Charlotte St,
London W1T 4QE
Originally published under the title
Rezepte gegen Cellulite

© Gräfe und Unzer Verlag GmbH
Munich. English translation copyright
© 2001 Gaia Books Ltd

Translated by First Edition Translations Ltd,
Cambridge, UK.

Editorial: Katherine Pate

Nutrition advisor: Angela Dowden

Reproduction: MRM Graphics Ltd,
Winslow, UK.
Printed in Singapore

ISBN 1 85675 172 4

A catalogue record for this book is available in
the British Library

10 9 8 7 6 5 4 3 2 1

Caution
The techniques and recipes in this book
are to be used at the reader's sole
discretion and risk.
Always consult a doctor if you are in doubt
about a medical condition.

Angelika Ilies
On completing her studies in ecological
nutrition, Hamburg-born Angelika Ilies spent a
short time in London, where she experienced
everyday editorial life in a famous publishing
house. Back in Germany, she entered her
chosen profession and became a key member of
the cookery department of Germany's largest
food magazine. Since 1989 she has worked
successfully as a freelance author and food
journalist.

Susie M. and **Pete Eising** have studios in
Munich (Germany) and Kennebunkport, Maine
(USA). They studied at the Munich Academy of
Photography, where in 1991 they founded their
own studio for food photography.

For this book:
Photographic layout:
Martina Görach
Food styling:
Monika Schuster

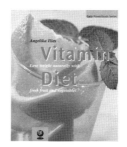

FENG SHUI COOKING
Recipes for harmony and health
Fahrnow, Fahrnow, and Sator
£4.99
ISBN 1 85675 146 5
More energy and wellbeing
from recipes that balance
your food.

BEAUTY FOOD
The natural way to looking good
Dagmar von Cramm
£4.99
ISBN 1 85675 141 4
Natural Beauty for skin and
hair - eating routines for a
fabulous complexion.

VITAMIN DIET
Lose weight naturally with fresh
fruit and vegetables
Angelika Ilies
£4.99
ISBN 1 85675 145 7
All the benefits of eating fresh
fruit and vegetables plus a
natural way to weight loss.

LOW CHOLESTEROL - LOW FAT
The easy way to reduce
cholesterol, stay slim and
enjoy your food
Döpp, Willrich and Rebbe
£4.99
ISBN 1 85675 166 X
Stay fit, slim and healthy
with easy-to-prepare
gourmet feasts.

ENERGY DRINKS
Power-packed juices, mixed,
shaken or stirred
Friedrich Bohlmann
£4.99
ISBN 1 85675 140 6
Fresh juices packed full of
goodness for vitality and
health.

ANTI STRESS
Recipes for acid-alkaline balance
Dagmar von Cramm
£4.99
ISBN 1 85675 155 4
A balanced diet to reduce
stress levels, maximise
immunity and help you
keep fit.

DETOX
Foods to cleanse and purify
from within
Angelika Ilies
£4.99
ISBN 1 85675 150 3
Detoxify your body as part of
your daily routine by eating
nutritional foods that have
cleansing properties.

MOOD FOOD
Recipes to cheer you up,
revitalize and comfort you
Marlisa Szwillus
£4.99
ISBN 1 85675 161 9
The best soul comforters,
the quickest revitalizers
and the most satisfying
stress busters.

To order the books featured on this page call 01453 752985, fax 01453 752987 with your credit/debit card details, or
send a cheque made payable to Gaia Books to Gaia Books Ltd., 20 High Street, Stroud, Glos., GL5 1AZ.
e-mail: gaiapub@dircon.co.uk or visit our website www.gaiabooks.co.uk